How to use this book

Follow the advice, in italics, given for you on each page.
Support the children as they read the text that is shaded in cream.
***Praise** the children at every step!*

Detailed guidance is provided in the Read Write Inc. Phonics Handbook

9 reading activities

Children:

Practise reading the speed sounds.

Read the green, red and challenge words for the story.

Listen as you read the introduction.

Discuss the vocabulary check with you.

Read the story.

Re-read the story and discuss the 'questions to talk about'.

Read the story with fluency and expression.

Answer the questions to 'read and answer'.

Practise reading the speed words.

Speed sounds

Consonants *Say the pure sounds (do not add 'uh').*

f ff ph	l ll le	m mm	n nn **gn**	r rr wr	s ss se c ce	v ve	z zz se	sh	th	ng nk

b bb	c k ck	d dd	g gg	h	j **g** ge	p pp	qu	t tt	w wh	x	y	ch tch

Vowels *Say the sounds in and out of order.*

at	hen head	in	on	up	day make	see tea happy	high smile lie find	blow home no

zoo brute blue	look	car	for door snore yawn	fair care	whirl nurse letter	shout cow	boy spoil

Each box contains one sound but sometimes more than one grapheme. Focus graphemes are ***circled****.*

Green words

Read in Fred Talk (pure sounds).

out found strange hair place slave huge beast spoke

floor poor sore thorn

saw raw law straw dawn paw claw jaw gnaw

Read in syllables.

Ro\`man stor\`y be\`fore mast\`er in\`side nev\`er shad\`ow aw\`ful

Read the root word first and then with the ending.

bone → bones bad → badly treat → treated

peace → peacefully shout → shouting open → opened

scorn → scornfully broke → broken crawl → crawled

yawn → yawned gnaw → gnawing

Red words

many could one are were other through

was

Challenge words

sword Androcles

The lion's paw

Introduction

Discuss the term 'One good turn deserves another'.
When has helping someone meant that something nice has happened to you in return?

A long, long time ago, in Roman times, a poor slave called Androcles runs away from his master. He finds a cave to sleep in but the cave is a lion's den. Androcles helps the lion and they become friends. After a while, Androcles decides to go back to his home. But he is thrown into prison by his master and made to fight lions in a lion pit (explain what a lion pit is like).

What will happen to Androcles now?

Story written by Gill Munton
Illustrated by Tim Archbold

Vocabulary check

Discuss the meaning (as used in the story) after the children have read each word.

	definition:	**sentence/phrase:**
den	*a cave where animals live*	*The cave was a lion's den!*
mighty	*large and powerful*	*The lion opened his mighty jaws.*
thorn	*sharp twig*	*A sharp thorn was stuck deep...*
paw	*animal's foot*	*...in the lion's paw.*
scornfully	*nastily*	*"You have broken the law," he shouted scornfully.*
slops	*horrid, watery soup*	*He had straw to sleep on and slops to eat.*
jeering	*shouting and teasing*	*There were thousands of people shouting and jeering.*

Punctuation to note in this story:

1. Capital letters to start sentences and full stops to end sentences

2. Capital letters for names

3. Exclamation marks to show anger, shock and surprise

4. 'Wait and see' dots...

5. Speech marks

The lion's paw

This is a story about a Roman slave called Androcles.
His master treated him so badly that, one day,
he ran away.

Androcles needed a place to sleep.
So when he saw a cave,
dug out of the hillside,
he crawled inside.

As Androcles lay resting, he saw
a pile of bones on the floor.
Then he saw a long, golden hair. A lion's hair!
The cave was a lion's den!

Before he could run away,
a shadow fell across the floor.
The lion was back!

The lion opened his mighty jaws,
Gnashing his teeth and flashing his claws,
And then he stretched out on the dusty floor.
Looked up at Androcles, held out his paw …

"Poor beast," said Androcles.

For a sharp thorn was stuck deep in the lion's paw.

He took the sore paw in his hands, and pulled the thorn until it came out. The lion yawned, and was soon snoring peacefully.

The lion woke at dawn and went hunting.
Soon, Androcles was feasting on fresh, raw meat,
and the lion was gnawing the bones.

Androcles and the lion lived happily in the cave for many months.

But Androcles was a man, not a lion,
and he needed to be with other men.
He shook the lion by the paw,
and set off back to Rome.

But his wicked master saw him.
"You have broken the law,"
he shouted scornfully,
"and you must be punished!"

Androcles was thrown into prison –
an awful place, with only straw to sleep on and slops to eat.

The next morning, the guard spoke to Androcles.
"You are going to be thrown to the lions," he said.

Androcles was given a sword and a helmet,
and pushed through a huge wooden door.
He found himself in a sort of circus ring,
with thousands of people shouting and jeering.

Then, across the ring,
he saw the lion – huge, growling and
angry.

A strange thing happened next.

The lion opened his mighty jaws,
Gnashing his teeth, and flashing his claws,
And then he stretched out on the dusty floor,
Looked up at Androcles, held out his paw.

It was the lion from the cave!

Androcles took the paw, and kissed it. There were loud cheers from the people. They had never seen a man kissing a lion's paw before! They began to chant: "Set them free! Set them free!"

Androcles and the loyal lion were freed, and lived together for ever more.

Questions to talk about

Re-read the page. Read the question to the children. Tell them whether it is a **FIND IT** *question or* **PROVE IT** *question.*

FIND IT	**PROVE IT**
✓ *Turn to the page*	✓ *Turn to the page*
✓ *Read the question*	✓ *Read the question*
✓ *Find the answer*	✓ *Find your evidence*
	✓ *Explain why*

Page 9:	FIND IT	*Why did Androcles run away?*
Page 10:	PROVE IT	*How did Androcles know he was in a lion's den?*
Page 11:	PROVE IT	*What did Androcles think the lion was going to do to him?* *Why was the lion really upset?*
Page 12:	PROVE IT	*Where does Androcles get his food from? How does he get on with the lion?*
Page 13:	PROVE IT	*Why does Androcles leave the lion?* *What happens to him when he goes back home?*
Page 14:	PROVE IT	*How do you think Androcles felt as he walked into the Arena?*
Page 15:	PROVE IT	*Why was Androcles safe in the end?*

Questions to read and answer

(Children complete without your help.)

1. Where did Androcles go when he ran away?

2. Why was the lion cross?

3. Why was Androcles thrown in prison?

4. What did Androcles expect the lion to do?

5. Why did the people want to set Androcles and the lion free?

Speed words

Children practise reading the words across the rows, down the columns and in and out of order clearly and quickly.

shouting	opened	huge	sore	badly
inside	dawn	awful	crawled	yawned
claws	raw	many	through	done
someone	one	other	are	were